HORRIBLE SCIENCE
TEACHERS' RESOURCES

ANIMALS

Nick Arnold • Tony De Saulles
additional material David Tomlinson

AUTHOR
Nick Arnold

ILLUSTRATIONS
Tony De Saulles

ADDITIONAL TEXT
David Tomlinson

EDITOR
Wendy Tse

ASSISTANT EDITORS
Charlotte Ronalds
Aileen Lalor

SERIES DESIGNER
Joy Monkhouse

DESIGNER
Catherine Mason

Designed using Adobe InDesign

Published by Scholastic Ltd
Villiers House
Clarendon Avenue
Leamington Spa
Warwickshire
CV32 5PR

www.scholastic.co.uk

Printed by Bell & Bain Ltd, Glasgow

1 2 3 4 5 6 7 8 9   4 5 6 7 8 9 0 1 2 3

British Library Cataloguing-in-Publication Data
A catalogue record for this book is available from the British Library.

ISBN 0-439-97181-0

TEACHERS' NOTES

Horrible Science Teachers' Resources: Animals is inspired by the Horrible Science book *Nasty Nature*. Each photocopiable takes a weird and wonderful excerpt from the original, as well as from *Evolve or Die*, *Explosive Experiments* and *The Awfully Big Quiz Book*, and expands on it to create a class-based teaching activity, fulfilling both National Curriculum and QCA objectives. The activities can be used individually or in a series as part of your scheme of work.

With an emphasis on research, experimentation and interpreting results, the activities will appeal to anyone even remotely curious about the Horrible world around us!

PART 1: DESCRIBING CREATURES

Page 11: Our animals

Learning objective

Making systematic observations.

Adults have young and these grow into adults, which in turn produce young.

Start the session by talking about animals the children have seen or may keep as pets, encouraging them to bring in pictures. Compare these animals to humans and make a list of similarities and differences, focusing on day-to-day care. Use photocopiable page 11 as the basis for group research, encouraging the children to present their creature-care booklet to the class.

Page 12: Describing animals

Learning objective

Different animals in different habitats.

There are different types of animals in the immediate environment.

Use any picture books or stories the children are familiar with and focus your class on how we perceive and describe different creatures, sometimes unfairly. Encourage the children to point out physical features of animals in the books, and widen the description to include information about habitat and behaviour. Use photocopiable page 12 to encourage the children to improve on one scientist's descriptions. Introduce the importance of the Linnaean system of naming plants and animals by classifying them in groups. As an extension include pictures and descriptions of other animals for a class safari park display.

Page 13: Size of an elephant!

Learning objective

Different animals in different habitats.

There are different types of animals in the immediate environment.

Use photocopiable page 13 as the start of a discussion about different sizes of creatures and how this affects their behaviour. Use class books and pictures of other animals to compare creatures from all over the world, both underwater and on land. Encourage the children to include humans to get an idea of where they fit in. As an extension make a concertina book of animals in ascending size, complete with any dimensions and other information.

Page 14: True or False quiz

Learning objective

Considering different sources of information.

Asking scientific questions.

Use photocopiable page 14 to encourage the children with their personal research, with rewards for the most weird and wonderful facts for a class book.

Answers: 1 Probably FALSE although some people swear they've seen it. Maybe it's a relative of the more famous Loch Ness Monster. The Swedish government has banned attempts to kill or capture the creature just in case it does exist.

2 TRUE. The horn is 15 cm (6 inches) long. The bird itself lives in marshes in tropical South America. You can hear its scream 3 km (2 miles) away.

3 TRUE.

4 TRUE. The golden tree snake can glide 46 metres (150 feet). The snake launches itself from a high branch and draws its underside in and pushes its body forward as it zooms through the air.

5 FALSE.
6 TRUE. It uses its fins to grab branches. Once in the trees it allows ants to crawl over its body. Then it leaps back in the river. The ants fall off the fish and float around in the water – to be gobbled at leisure!
7 FALSE.
8 TRUE. It's the duck-billed platypus! This strange creature is actually an unusual species of mammal that looks like a mole pretending to be a duck. The puzzling platypus has also got detectors that sense electrical waves given off by small creatures at the bottom of muddy rivers. Classifying this freaky creature could drive a naturalist quackers.

Page 15: Drink like a cat!

Learning objective
Thinking creatively in science.
Asking scientific questions.

Start this session by talking about how we eat and compare it to the way other animals eat. Use the experiment on photocopiable page 15 to focus the children on why an animal may eat in a particular way, making links with how it moves. Look at the diets of different animals and discuss how this can influence the way they eat. For example, look at the eating habits of giraffes. Use the children's ideas about movement and eating to introduce the concept of different families of creatures, looking at animals that eat similar foods in similar ways. As an extension try an animal café with children eating or drinking in the roles of different animals.
Note! Ensure all food is brought from home in case of allergies.
Answer: b) Most humans can't make the right shape with their tongues.

Page 16: See like a rabbit!

Learning objective
Making systematic observations.
Making predictions.

Start this session by asking your class to look around them, encouraging them to describe how they use their eyes. Use a range of different animals to contrast with humans, such as bats, owls and snails. Recap any work you may have done on predators and prey and explain to the children that many animals have adapted their sight in order to survive. Rabbits have a far wider field of view from humans and photocopiable page 16 will help recreate this. Encourage your class to write and draw their descriptions and to play 'Fox and Rabbit' to test out the usefulness of their creations.

Page 17: Animals overseas

Learning objective
Thinking creatively in science.
Asking scientific questions.

Talk to your class about how scientists have learned more about different creatures since travel has become easier. Comparing creatures has lead to major scientific advances, such as Charles Darwin's theories of evolution. Encourage the children to take the modern-day equivalent of Darwin's epic world voyage on the *Beagle* by using the Internet and books to look at animals not usually seen in the UK. They can link this to any visits to the zoo they may have experienced, and record their findings on photocopiable page 17.

Page 18: Evolution

Learning objective
Making systematic observations.
Making predictions.

Start this session by introducing the idea that creatures have changed very slowly over many thousands of years and continue to do so. Humans are taller than in Henry VIII's time due to good diet, but true evolution is embedded in our DNA and takes longer. Encourage your class to describe the changes they see on photocopiable page 18 and to make thoughtful predictions about how these creatures (including humans) might continue to evolve.

Page 19: Cheeky monkey!

Learning objective

Making systematic observations.
Making generalisations.

Recap any discussion you may have had in class about different creatures being related to each other, asking the children which animals move and look most like humans. Use photocopiable page 19 to focus your class on their physical and behavioural links with chimpanzees, encouraging them to make detailed comparisons (for example, number of fingers and length of limbs). As an extension hold a movement workshop, recreating different creatures' behaviour, comparing it again to humans.

Page 20: Rabbits' recipe

Learning objective

Identifying locally occurring animals.
Understanding interdependence and survival.

Use a video or written extract from *Watership Down* to encourage your class to 'think' themselves into role as another animal, focusing them on real day-to-day issues such as feeding and survival. Use the 'Rabbits' recipe for success' on photocopiable page 20 to consider how such factors as fur colour can influence an animal's likelihood of survival. Ask the children to write a report on a day in the life of a brown, black or white rabbit.

Survival scores: a) Two years if you are a brown rabbit – you'll blend in easily against the field. One year if you're black – you don't stand out too much. Almost no time at all if you're white – you'll stick out like a sore thumb and make easy prey for passing stoats.

b) Two years if you're brown or black. You won't be easily snapped up by passing owls. It's bad news if you're white, though. They'll see you easily, so you won't have long to live.

c) Two years if you're brown. Your fur is too dull for a fashionable fur coat. Almost no time at all for black or white rabbits, though. Your handsome fur is far too attractive.

d) Two years if you're white. You blend perfectly with the snow. But brown or black rabbits won't survive long – the stoats are on their tails in no time.

Add up your scores. For a brown rabbit, six years; for a black rabbit, two years; for a white rabbit… well, if they're lucky they can live for two years too. So it's easy to see why black or white rabbits are rare.

Page 21: Descriptions

Learning objective

Thinking creatively in science.
Words naming features of animals.

Use photocopiable page 21 to focus your class on the different attributes that animals have and how we use these in modern sayings. Encourage the children to come up with their own examples and ideas and collate them in a class dictionary of quotes and sayings.

Page 22: Stunning senses and skills

Learning objective

Testing ideas through observation.
Words naming features of animals.

Explain to the children that the Stunning sense statistics on photocopiable page 22 are true, but only tell half the story. Look at familiar animals, asking what attributes they may have and how humans compare. Encourage the children to present their findings to the rest of the class.

Page 23 & 24: Simple sorting & Super sorting

Learning objective

Making and using keys.
Using keys to identify animals.

Start this session by looking at pictures of different animals and ask the children to sort them (for example, according to size or diet). Explain that we can use a sorting tree to help us, using photocopiable page 23 as an example. Encourage the children to try this method in pairs. Ask them to choose four animals and create their own sorting tree using yes/no questions. Use photocopiable page 24 to allow more considered individual work, encouraging the children to design their own sorting tree for the animals you showed them at the start of the session.

PART 2:

CREATURES IN THEIR HABITATS

Page 25: Nasty habitats!

Learning objective

Different animals are found in different habitats and are suited to them.
Observing conditions of a habitat.

Start this session by talking about the places that we live and what we like about them. Humans have always settled in locations that have water and where they can find shelter and food. We have refined this so that homes have water and warmth, and shops deliver food. Encourage the children to widen this debate to include animals that they are familiar with, and extend it to research very different habitats. Use photocopiable page 25 to record their thoughts and research. As an extension design a man-made habitat for one of the creatures, deciding which features are most important to replicate.

Page 26: Migration

Learning objective

Different animals are found in different habitats and are suited to them.
Making predictions of animals.

Start by talking about places that your class may have visited and reasons for taking these holidays. Focus your class on temperature, using an atlas and photocopiable page 26 as an introduction to the idea of migration. Recap any work you may have done using block graphs in order to record this data.

Page 27: Conservation debate

Learning objective

Ways in which living things need protection.
To treat animals with care and sensitivity.

Use photocopiable page 27 to discuss the effects that changes in habitats can have on the creatures that live there. Widen this to include other reasons that creatures may be threatened. Encourage your class to work in groups and to record their thoughts and feelings in preparation for a class debate, deciding what the motion is to be and taking a vote at the end.

Page 28: Snail's-eye view

Learning objective

Testing ideas through observation.
Making predictions of animals.

Start this session by recapping any work that you may have done about different creatures, linking this to the differing view they will have of the same world (for example, a bird's-eye view contrasted with that of a human). Go through the experiment on photocopiable page 28, recording thoughts and observations, encouraging the children to complete the story. As an extension adapt the story into a strip cartoon for a display, including photographs from the snail's viewpoint.

Page 29: Comparing habitats

Learning objective

Different animals are found in different habitats and are suited to them.
Observing conditions of a habitat.

Use photocopiable page 29 to focus your class on the huge range of habitats different creatures choose, asking the children to add examples of their own. Encourage the children to extend this activity by grouping together animals according to their habitat and to examine these creatures for common features.

Page 30: Keeping clean

Learning objective

Different animals are found in different habitats and are suited to them.
Making predictions of animals in their habitat.

Ask your children how they keep themselves clean

and why it is a good idea to do this regularly. Broaden the discussion to include animals, using pigs as an example. Pigs are naturally clean creatures, however humans often keep them in muddy conditions. Use this example to show that all creatures have a cleaning regime according to their needs. Use photocopiable page 30 to focus the children on specific animals, encouraging them to present their adverts in groups.

Page 31: Fish facts

Learning objective

Thinking creatively to try to explain how things work.
Enquiry in environmental and technological contexts.

Talk to your class about any trips to an aquarium they may have experienced, encouraging them to describe what they saw even if they do not remember many names. Link this to the more common fish we see around us, or indeed eat. Use photocopiable page 31 as a starting point for individual research or a class quiz.

Answers: 1, **2**, **4**, **6** TRUE; **3**, **5** FALSE.

PART 3: LIFE CYCLES

Page 32: Life cycles

Learning objective

The main stages of the life cycle.
Adults have young and these grow into adults which in turn produce young.

Start by recapping any work your class may have done about the human life cycle and growing older, relating their present stage to your discussion. Use photocopiable page 32 to focus your class on the life cycle of the frog, explaining that the cartoon joins the cycle halfway through. Discuss what happens before the tadpole hatches: the mother frog lays the eggs; she leaves the eggs in the pond; the eggs develop; the tadpole emerges. Encourage your class to complete the cycle, labelling their drawings for class display.

Page 33: Inside an egg

Learning objective

The main stages of the life cycle.
Adults have young and these grow into adults which in turn produce young.

Start this session by cracking open an egg and asking the children to describe what they see, explaining what the yolk is used for if the egg has a chick inside. Use the experiment on photocopiable page 33 to focus the children on this part of the life cycle and to compare it to the human experience.

Answers: a) The shell lets in air but not water. The air passes into the developing chick's bloodstream AND **c)** An air bubble forms in the blunt end of the egg. Half a mark for this answer because the chick only breathes this air for a few days before it hatches.

Page 34: Reproduction

Learning objective

The main stages of the life cycle.
Adults have young and these grow into adults which in turn produce young.

Cut open a peeled hard-boiled egg so that the children can examine what is inside, explaining that it has solidified in the boiling process. Make it clear that the eggs that we eat don't have chicks in them! Use photocopiable page 34 to focus your class on different creatures and how they are born, relating this to different life cycles. Ask them if they have any pets (such as cats, dogs and rabbits) that have had babies. This activity can be used in conjunction with the 'Rabbits' recipe for success' on photocopiable page 20. As an extension, encourage your class to compile a huge class-display life cycle comparing different creatures at similar points. Mount on a circle of card so that the cycle can turn.

Page 35: Rabbit calculations

Learning objective

The main stages of the life cycle.
Adults have young and these grow into adults which in turn produce young.

Recap any work your class may have done contrasting the gestation and birth rate of common animals, relating this to the human experience. Encourage the children to show their working out, reminding them that their calculations will be valuable even if some of their answers are not right. As an extension have a numeracy quiz in ability groups using animal facts and figures; compile the questions into a class book.

PART 4: FOOD AND FOOD CHAINS

Page 36: Food chains

Learning objective

Using food chains to show feeding relationships in a habitat and that most start with a green plant. Identifying food sources and structures of food chains.

Start this session by looking at food packets brought in by your class. Trace the journey the food has made from farm to factory to supermarket to home and then onto their plate. Explain that this collection of events is a chain. Take a look at where that food came from in the very beginning and construct a simple food chain, using the children's favourite foods. Use photocopiable page 36 to focus the children on non-processed foods and our own place in the food chain.

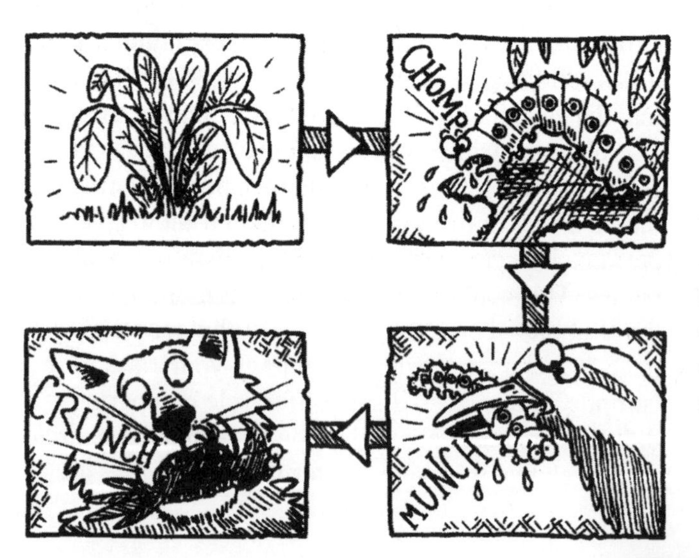

Page 37: Hunting

Learning objective

Using food chains to show feeding relationships in a habitat and that most start with a green plant. Identifying food sources and structures of food chains.

Talk to the children about animals that eat meat (dogs, cats and so on) and how they obtain it in the wild. Use photocopiable page 37 to focus the children on the hunting instinct of lions, explaining that this is replicated in zoos by throwing fresh meat and including regular 'starvation days' to replicate the wild. Use the answer options for class debate.

Answers: 1 b)

2 a) Lions show a lot of teamwork when hunting. Some scientists believe that this is an illusion and all the lions are doing their own thing.

3 c)

4 b) Males are bigger and stronger than the females. If there's not enough food for everyone the lionesses and cubs starve.

5 c) Nasty but true. The male wants the lioness to look after his youngsters once they are born. The lioness wants the male to protect her from other males.

6 b) A starving lion will eat anything so be careful if you're in the area.

Page 38: Food web

Learning objective

Using food chains to show feeding relationships in a habitat and that most start with a green plant. Identifying food sources and structures of food chains.

Recap any work you may have done on food chains, using photocopiable page 38 to broaden understanding to include food webs, grouping creatures by habitat as well as the food chain. Talk about creatures that live under the sea, focusing on those that humans eat. Use this information to construct a food web for underwater creatures, allowing for dry-land predators.

Page 39: Who eats what?

Learning objective

Using food chains to show feeding relationships in a habitat and that most start with a green plant. Identifying food sources and structures of food chains.

Start by looking at the foods that we enjoy eating, using photocopiable page 39 to focus the children on different diets required by different animals. Recap the words *herbivore*, *omnivore* and *carnivore*, encouraging the children to find their own examples of each and to try them out on each other.

Answers: 1 a) The kite will only eat snails. So if there aren't any to peck the kite gets peckish instead. **2 b)** Rabbits have a side pocket in their guts filled with bacteria where food rots and becomes easier to digest. By eating its dung the rabbit gives the food a second chance to rot and become more nourishing. **3 e)** No one knows why they do this, but the feathers may help the bird sick up fish bones. **4 f)** Yes – its own brothers and sisters. There are two kinds of tadpoles. Harmless little plant eaters and cannibals with sharp teeth. **5 c)** An octopus will eat its own leg if it's hungry enough. Luckily for the octopus it grows another. **6 g)** Elephants visit a cave on Mount Elgon in East Africa to chew chunks of rock. Scientists think the rock contains minerals that keep the elephants healthy. **7 d)** I'd stick to honey!

PART 5:

EXTINCT OR ENDANGERED?

Page 40: Extinct or endangered?

Learning objective

Ways in which living things need protection.
To treat animals with care and sensitivity.

Start by defining the words *extinct* and *endangered.* Use photocopiable page 40 as a starting point for a discussion in groups on extinct and endangered animals, asking the children to report their views. Encourage the children to work out reasons why certain animals are endangered and to use this information to compile a guide explaining how we can ensure their survival. As an extension ask the children to design posters putting across their ideas in order to persuade others.

Page 41 & 42: The tiger must die! 1&2

Learning objective

Ways in which living things need protection.
To treat animals with care and sensitivity.

Read this story as part of your literacy session, explaining to the children that it is based on fact. Discuss possible endings from the options given at the end, asking the children to explain their reasons. Encourage the children to continue the story to the conclusion they have chosen before you reveal the answer. Contrast the different endings written by the children and compile a class book to go with the original story.

Answer: b) The Director's bosses still wouldn't allow him to shoot the tiger so he came round to Arjan Singh's idea. The tiger ate the food provided and stopped attacking people. Nowadays many man-eating tigers are moved to areas away from where people live.

Page 43: The tiger must die! 3

Learning objective

Ways in which living things need protection
To treat animals with care and sensitivity.

Use the information box on photocopiable page 43 to extend the debate from the original story, encouraging your class to express a range of views. Recap any play scripts they may have used and the format for writing in this style. Ask the children to continue the story in play form, splitting it into scenes and casting group members in role. Perform the scenes for the class, deciding which work most successfully and combining them into a class play for performance.

PART 6:
QUIZ & ASSESSMENT

Page 44 & 45: Wordsearch clues & grid

Learning objective

Considering different sources.
Using available sources.

Use photocopiable pages 44 and 45 as the basis of a class challenge, putting together the knowledge and research skills they have accumulated in their science sessions.

Answer: c) No fish in the world can do **a)** or **b)**.

Page 46: Bears beware quiz!

Learning objective

Thinking creatively to try to explain how things work, establishing links between cause and effect.
Enquiry in environmental and technological contexts.

Ask your class to talk about animals that they know are dangerous, encouraging them to include any safety ideas. Use photocopiable page 46 to focus the class on the DOs and DON'Ts on the sheet. Broaden this to include other animals and encourage the children to work in pairs, presenting their quizzes to the class.

Answers:

DOs

2 Bears can sniff out blood – and they think that an injured human might make an easy meal.
3 Feel free – the bears know where you are anyway and the sound might frighten them away. But if you manage to spot one before it sees you, you might want to stay quiet for fear of annoying it.
6 Slowly does it!
8 Grizzly bears lose interest but you might have to put up with one of them munching your leg if it's hungry. Try not to wriggle too much if that happens. Black bears might eat the rest of you so only pretend to be dead if you can't get away.
9 This is good advice when dealing with grizzlies, but black bears climb and if one rips your trousers off you could have a bear behind.

DON'Ts

1 This is *berry* bad advice – the bears normally eat berries so they'll be hungry and more likely to attack.
4 Bears love chocolate and can sniff it out from a distance. Although the bear will happily accept your chocolate it might absent-mindedly walk off with your arm too.
5 The smell is bound to attract bears. If you've already eaten the hamburgers, they can smell the food on your clothes and breath.
7 In bear language this is like saying: 'OI, CUP-CAKE, YOU LOOK LIKE MY TEDDY!'
10 This is when the females are most vicious.

Page 47: Animal spotter's quiz

Learning objective

Thinking creatively to try to explain how things work, establishing links between cause and effect.
Enquiry in environmental and technological contexts.

Answers: 1 c) A ring-tailed cat is a racoon-like creature (and definitely not a cat).
2 d) The naked mole rat is neither a mole nor a rat. It's more like a nude African guinea pig that burrows underground. One scientist called it 'a sabre-toothed sausage' – I hope your pet guinea pig is better looking!
3 b) Crayfish aren't fish – they're related to lobsters. Both are crustaceans.
4 e) Fireflies aren't flies, they're beetles. (And if you know all about flies you could be the school swat.)
5 a) Glass-snakes are lizards…
6 g) … and so are horned toads.
7 f) A civet cat is related to the mongoose (but nothing to do with a dead elk – that's a gone moose).

Page 48: Fishy accumulator quiz

Learning objective

Thinking creatively to try to explain how things work, establishing links between cause and effect.
Enquiry in environmental and technological contexts.

Use photocopiable page 38 to focus your class on the work that they have done about underwater creatures. Use this quiz structure as the basis of individual research and encourage the children to work in pairs, trying out their own quiz questions on classmates. Compile them for a class Accumulator Quiz Book.

NAME ______________________ DATE ______________________

Our animals

Brute force. Beastly behaviour. Animal cunning. Whenever humans have anything nasty to say to one anther they drag animals into it. And animals bring out the worst in some humans, which can lead to nasty situations…

The science of animals can also provide some nasty surprises (and we're not talking about your brutish, wolfish, slavering teacher here). What, for example, about the odd words scientists use to describe our four-legged friends? They certainly leave a nasty taste in your mouth – when you don't understand them.

- Animals look very different from humans yet they can share similar behaviour to us.
- Compare an animal and compare it to humans. List the similarities and differences .

Similarities | Differences

- Create a creature-care booklet and remember to include information on feeding and caring for your animal.

NAME ______________________ DATE ______________

DESCRIBING ANIMALS

- Scientists discover more about creatures as time goes on.
- A Swedish scientist called Carl Linnaeus was the very first to group animals into a logical order. He studied them closely and grouped similar animals together.

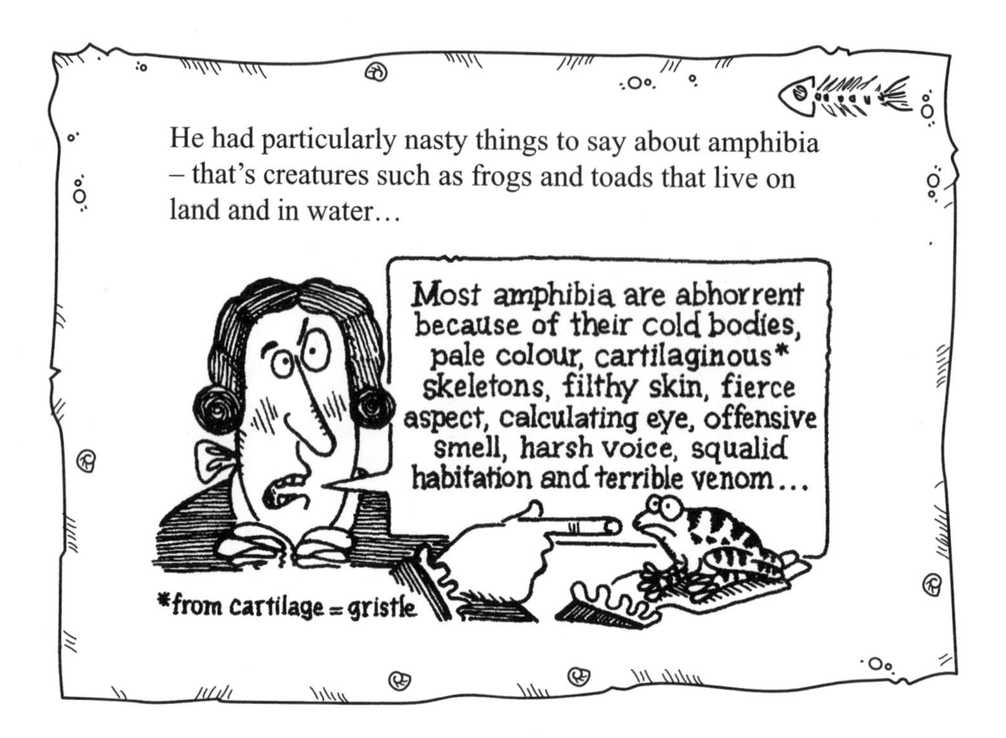

- See if you can improve on Carl Linnaeus's description of frogs and toads.

____

____

____

- Now try and describe the animals below. Refer to size, shape, colour, touch and even smell! Add any other information that you can find.

SIZE OF AN ELEPHANT!

Little and large facts
The largest animal that has ever lived is the blue whale. This creature can grow to 33 metres (110 feet) long and weigh 80 tonnes (79 tons). That's 24 times the size of an elephant and even bigger than the biggest dinosaur. Inside the blue whale there are over 8,500 litres (15,000 pints) of blood protected by a layer of fat 61 cm (2 feet) thick. But here's a nasty thought: since 1900 human hunters have brought at least 364,000 of these stupendous creatures to a horrible end.

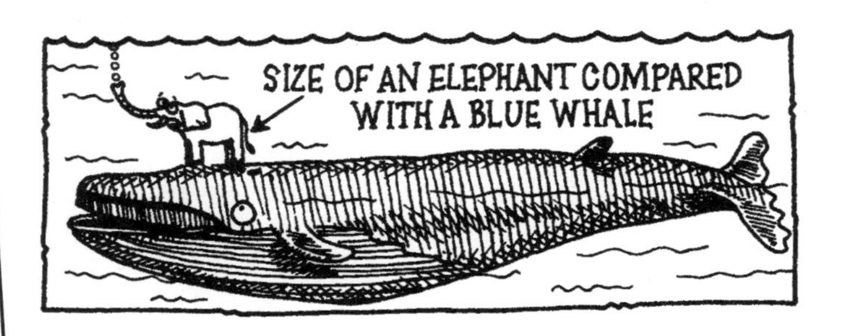

Compare that with… Helena's humming bird. It's only 5.7 cm (2¼ inches) from bill to tail and weighs a mere 2 grams (0.07 ounces). This tiny scrap of a creature lives off sweet, sticky nectar from flowers.

The Marshall Islands goby is a tiddler of a fish that lives in the Pacific Ocean. It is only 1.27 cm (½ inch) long.

- Cut out the three pictures and put the creatures in size order, starting with the smallest.
- Look at other animals of different sizes. Where do they fit in to your creature size scale?
- Include humans in your scale. Are they amongst the smallest or largest creatures on Earth?

Bet you never knew!
There are currently about 10,000,000,000,000,000, 000,000,000,000,000,000 (that's 10 billion, trillion, trillion) animals on Earth (give or take a few million) and they come in all shapes and sizes.

True or False quiz

- Some of these statements are true and some are false – but which are which?

Weird wildlife quiz

1 The storsjoodjuret is an ugly-looking, long-necked reptile that skulks around in Lake Storsjön in Sweden. It's between 10-20 metres (32-65 feet) long. TRUE/FALSE

2 There's a type of bird with a horn on its head like a unicorn. It's called a 'horned screamer'. TRUE/FALSE

3 The Jack Dempsey fish is named after a famous American boxer. This small South American freshwater fish got its name because it enjoys ramming into other fish and stealing their eggs. TRUE/FALSE

4 There's a type of snake that can fly short distances. TRUE/FALSE

5 The Malaysian two-headed bat has a lump on its back that looks just like an extra head. This fools owls that attempt to bite the bat's head off in mid-air. TRUE/FALSE

6 The Indian climbing perch is a fish that climbs trees. TRUE/FALSE

7 The Iberian 'singing' goat is an excellent mimic. (That's the posh name for someone who copies voices.) It has been known to imitate the yodelling calls of local mountaineers! TRUE/FALSE

8 There's a creature that hangs out in Australian rivers with a bill like a duck and fur like a beaver. It lays eggs like a bird and has poisonous spines like a lizard. TRUE/FALSE

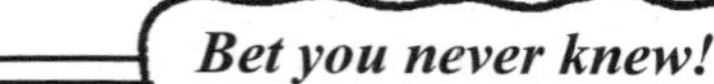

Bet you never knew!
In 1983 scientists discovered a super microbe lurking in a cavern in Arkansas, USA. It's a blob of jelly made up of millions of amoebae that slither along like a single creature! Its favourite food is bat droppings but it sometimes attacks lumps of fungus. It sends out fighter amoebae to eat the fungus.

NAME ____________________ DATE ____________________

Drink like a cat!

What you need:
Yourself
A bowl of water
A mirror

All you do is:
1 Look at your tongue in the mirror. A cat can fold up the sides of its tongue to make a shovel shape. Can you do this?

2 Try lapping the water. You then have to flick the water into the back of your throat with your tongue. How easy is this?
a) No problem at all.
b) It's impossible to get more than a few drops of liquid in your mouth.
c) Totally impossible. Luckily the cat came and drank the water.

- Some animals eat and move very differently to us. Others are more similar.
- Can you think of any? Draw them here and add any information that you can find.

Similar eaters!	Similar movers!
Different eaters!	Different movers!

- Do any of your animals move **and** eat similarly to humans? Why do you think this is?

NAME ______________________ DATE ______________________

SEE LIKE A RABBIT!

- Try Dr Will D. Beest's experiment on a rabbit's-eye view.

WHAT I NEEDED:
A PIECE OF METALLIC SHINY CARD FROM AN ART SHOP. (IF I HADN'T FOUND THE SHINY CARD, I WOULD HAVE CUT ORDINARY CARD TO SIZE AND USED STICKY TAPE TO STICK KITCHEN FOIL OVER IT.)

SOME SCISSORS

WHAT I DID:

1 I cut a piece of shiny card 30 cm (12 inches) long by 9 cm (3.5 inches) high.

2 Then I cut a nose shape as shown.

SHINY SIDE FACING ME

3 Finally I placed the card over my nose and with the shiny surface facing my eyes.
I bent the ends slightly away from my face.

RESULT:
Wow – I could see what was going on to each side of me. It was like having eyes on the sides of my head!

SPOOKY!

- What differences do you think you will notice between seeing like a rabbit and seeing normally?

____

- What did you see?

____

Rabbit's eye view

Left — Right

- What were the main differences you noticed? Write your results in a report.

REMARKS:
Animals like rabbits have eyes on the side of their heads to spot other creatures sneaking up on them. Hunting animals like foxes have eyes at the front so that they can judge distances and leap on top of their prey!

YUM YUM!

GULP!

NAME ______________________ DATE ______________________

Animals overseas

NAME: Giant tortoise

HABITAT: The Galapagos Islands

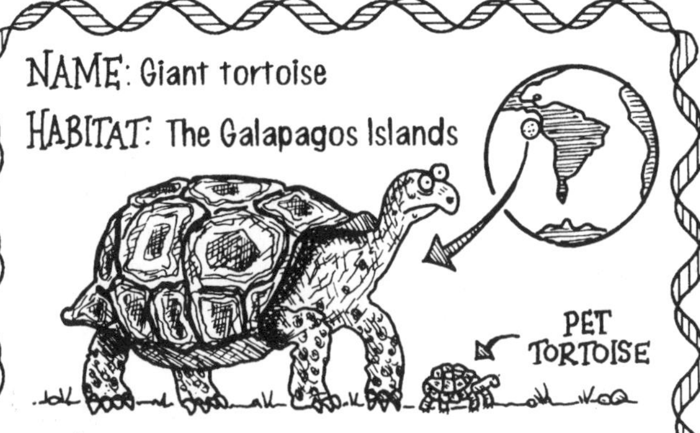

A single Galapagos giant tortoise can weigh 250kg. It takes eight men to lift one.

Sailors used to ride on them for fun. Darwin discovered that their top speed was about four miles per day.

Eleven different species of Galapagos tortoise survive today, each on its own Galapagos Island. Sadly, there's only one giant tortoise left on the island of Pinta. He's a male, called Lonesome George. A reward of $10,000 has been offered to anyone who can find a genuine female Pinta giant tortoise to keep Lonesome George company.

- Spanish sailors discovered giant tortoises when they landed on the Galapagos Islands 960km off the coast of Ecuador in South America in 1535.
- In the 1830s, Charles Darwin noted the differences among the species of giant tortoises.
- Choose a country from your atlas.
- Use books and the Internet to discover a creature living in that part of the world. Write a fact file below.

Name:

Country:

Habitat:

Diet:

Description:

Fascinating facts:

- Where in the world? Draw a globe here, highlighting the country your creature lives in.

- Draw your creature here.

NAME ____________________ DATE ____________________

EVOLUTION

- Charles Darwin collected animals from all over the world and worked out links between them. However, he and his crew aboard HMS *Beagle* did eat some of them...

- His idea was that creatures changed over thousands and millions of years. Look at this cartoon. What changes do you see? Describe the stages in your own words.

____

____

____

____

- Charles Darwin developed his theory of evolution, starting with amoebae and ending with mammals.

- Look at the cartoon of Darwin and his thought chain. Write the similarities and differences between each example along the chain.

NAME ______________________ DATE ______________________

Cheeky monkey!

- Charles Darwin was the first scientist to discover that humans, who belong to the hominid family, and chimpanzees shared the same distant ancestor – but they evolved different skills.

- Now we are very different!

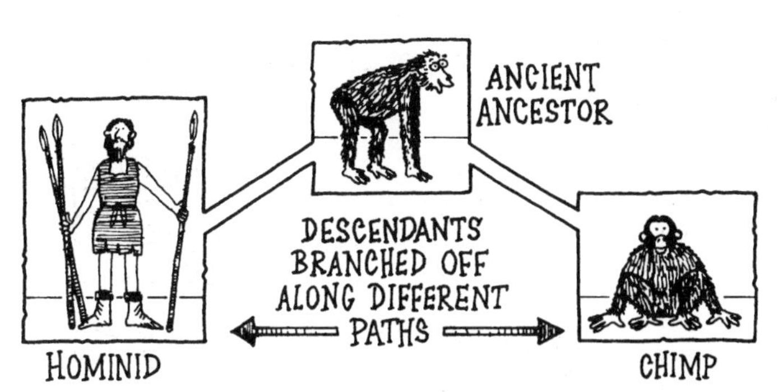

- Draw a human and a chimpanzee. Study them very carefully and note down the differences and similarities in how they look and how they behave.

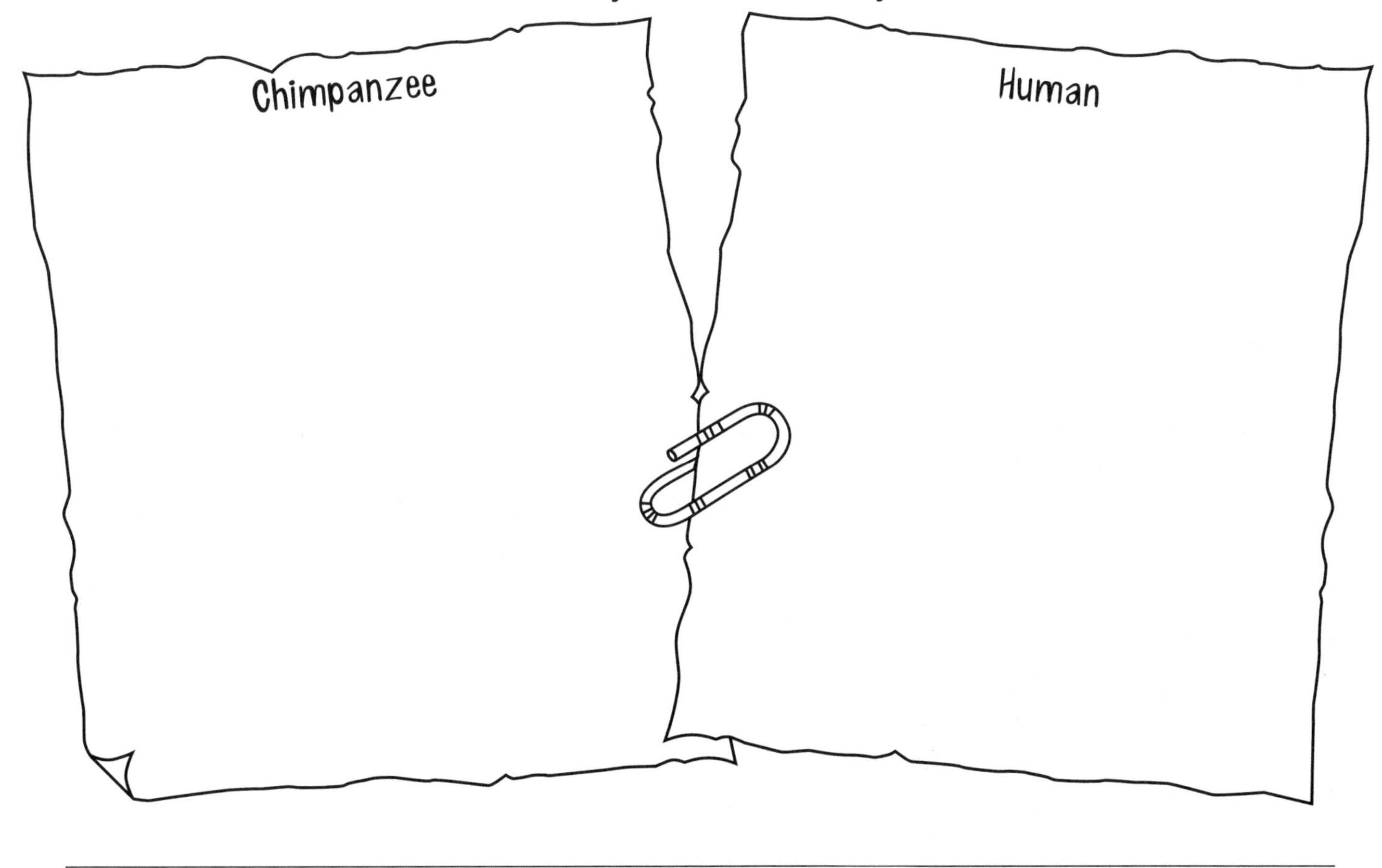

____

____

____

NAME ______________________ DATE ______________________

Rabbits' recipe

- Read the 'Rabbits' recipe for success' below.

Rabbits breed like, well, like rabbits, really. *Very* fast. Each one can produce around 50 baby bunnies each year.

The population of animals in a species tends to increase as long as there's plenty of food, water and somewhere to live. When these start to run out, life gets tough. Animals have to compete against other members of their own species in order to survive.

Suppose you were a rabbit. OK, so it's not that simple, but give it a try. Which would you rather be? A brown rabbit, a black rabbit or a white rabbit?

Choose your colour now, then see how long you'd survive: Imagine…

a) You're foraging for the nice juicy vegetables in a ploughed field.
b) You're out at night – are you protected from danger?
c) Humans are hunting for rabbit fur. Are you safe?
d) There's thick snow on the ground, and the stoats are sniffing around for a tasty snack.

- It's not easy being a rabbit!
- Imagine you are a brown, black or white rabbit. How would your fur colour affect you?
- Now write a day in your life as a rabbit. Include ideas about feeding, drinking, habitat, hunting and dangers, as well as your friends and relatives!
- Plan your report below.

NAME ______________________ DATE ______________________

DESCRIPTIONS

- We often use similes, analogy and metaphor when writing or describing people or places.
- Sometimes we use examples of animals to make our descriptions even more memorable.

- If you say someone is a 'bird brain' it means you don't think they are too clever, as birds have smaller brains than humans. Try matching these sayings to the animals below.

Fast as a ______________________

Big as an ______________________

Small as a ______________________

Swims like a ______________________

Elephant Fish Mouse Cheetah

- Now try making up your own.

Fierce as a ______________________

Tall as a ______________________

Clever as a ______________________

Jumps like a ______________________

Kicks like a ______________________

Sings like a ______________________

Flies like a ______________________

Stunning senses and skills

- Some animals can do things better than humans.
- But humans are better at other skills, such as talking and making tools, than some animals.
- Compile a Stunning skills guide comparing humans to animals to show that we can come out on top too!

STUNNING SENSE STATISTICS

ANIMAL SENSES	HUMAN SENSES 
SUPERSNIFFERS When you walk about in bare feet you leave 4 billionths of a gramme of sweat in each footprint. To a dog this stinks like a cheesy old pair of socks that haven't been washed for a month.	**DON'T SMELL TOO WELL** A human's sense of smell is one million times weaker than a dog's. EVEN THOUGH HIS NOSE IS TWICE AS BIG
EAGLE EYES A golden eagle can see a rabbit on the ground up to 3.2km (2 miles) away.	**A SIGHT FOR SORE EYES** Some humans trip over rabbits.
A NASTY TASTE IN THE MOUTH Ugly catfish that lurk at the bottom of South American rivers have 100,000 taste buds in their tongues. That's how they find food in the murky mud.	**TOTALLY TASTELESS** Humans only have 8,000 taste buds – that's half as many as a pig. (This may explain why pigs don't enjoy school dinners but some humans do.)
HEAR, HERE 1. A dog's ear has 17 muscles so it can turn in any direction. 2. The Californian leaf-nosed bat can hear the footsteps of insects.	**HARD OF HEARING HUMANS** 1. Humans only have nine ear muscles and most people can't even waggle theirs. 2. Can you? NO!
A TOUCH OF MAGIC Seals use their ultra-sensitive whiskers to pick up tiny movements in the water caused by another creature.	**A TOUCHY SUBJECT** Human whiskers don't even twitch. IT'S TRUE!
STRANGE SENSES 1. Animals can predict earthquakes. The German scientist Ernst Killian found that dogs howl several minutes before a quake strikes. 2. The American knife-fish produces an electric signal 300 times every second. This creates a force field around the animal. A disturbance in the field warns the fish there's another creature about.	**SENSELESS** 1. Weedy humans can't accurately predict earthquakes even using sophisticated scientific instruments. 2. Er . . . OK. YOU WIN!

NAME ______________________ DATE ______________________

SIMPLE SORTING

- We can sort animals by observing them closely.
- Name these animals by answering the questions in this simple sorting tree.

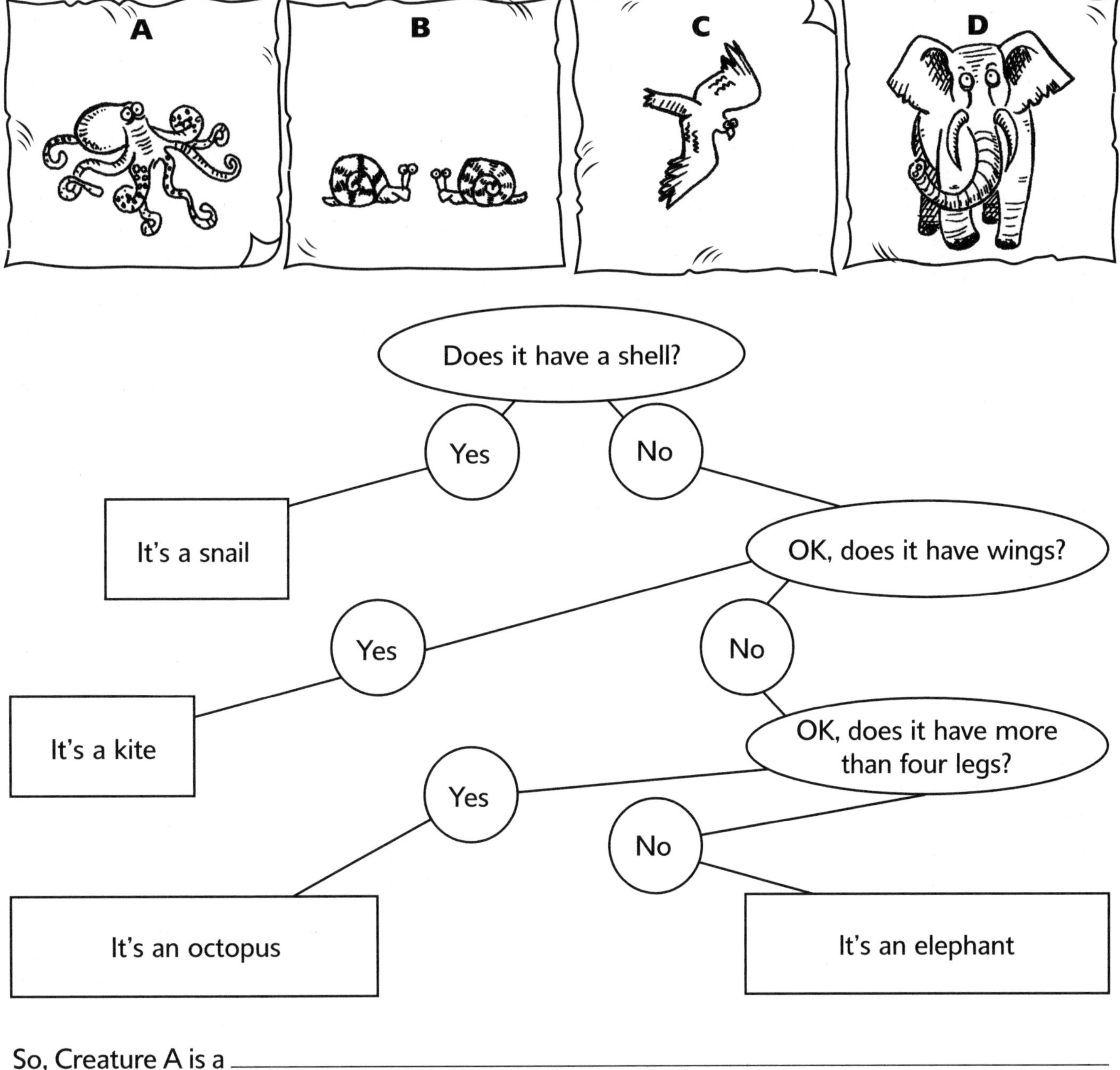

So, Creature A is a ______________________

Creature B is a ______________________

Creature C is a ______________________

Creature D is a ______________________

NAME ______________________ DATE ______________

SUPER SORTING

- Look at these creatures.

- Draw and label the creatures in the correct boxes, using the sorting tree to help you.

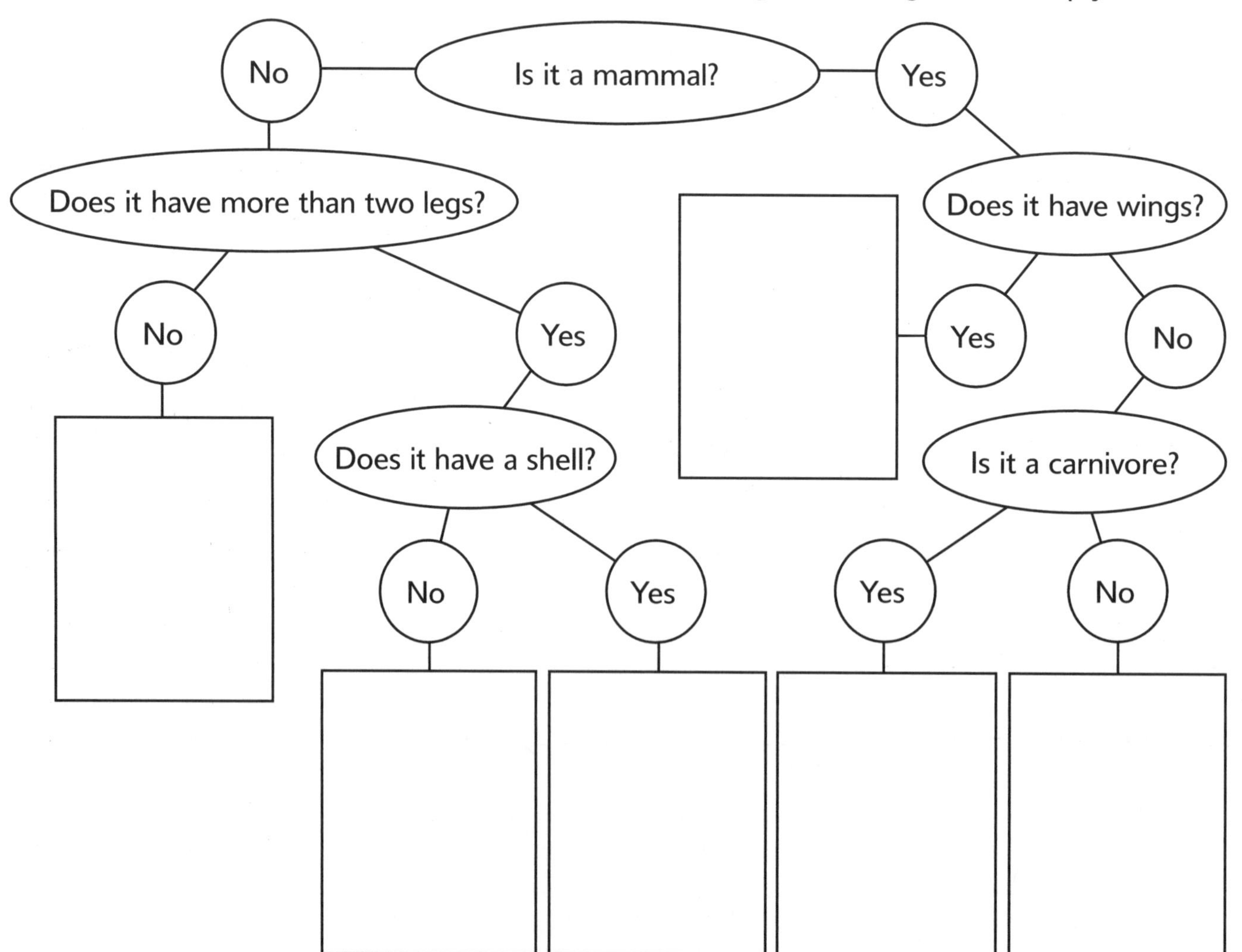

- Try making your own sorting tree for different animals.

NAME ____________________ DATE ____________________

Nasty habitats!

- Animals are found everywhere that you can imagine and a few places that you wouldn't want to. Animal habitats range from deserts and rainforests to coral reefs and stinking swamps.

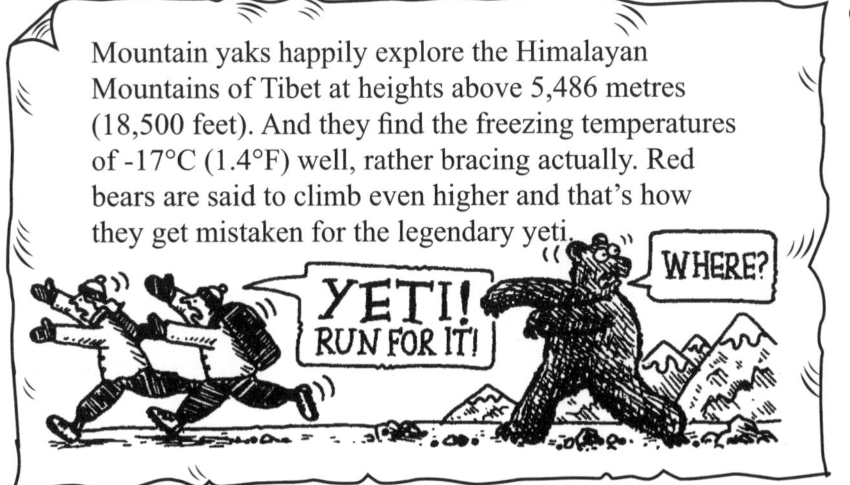

- Red bears and yaks are not the only creatures to live in unusual places! Choose one of these habitats and put a circle around it.

Desert

Rainforest

Coral reef

Stinking swamp

- Now use books or the Internet to help you create a data file on the creatures that live there. You can use these headings to help you collate information.

- Draw the creatures below.

Creature's name: ____________________

What it looks like: ____________________

What it eats: ____________________

Why it likes this habitat: ____________________

Creature's name: ____________________

What it looks like: ____________________

What it eats: ____________________

Why it likes this habitat: ____________________

Creature's name: ____________________

What it looks like: ____________________

What it eats: ____________________

Why it likes this habitat: ____________________

NAME ______________________________ DATE ______________________

MIGRATION

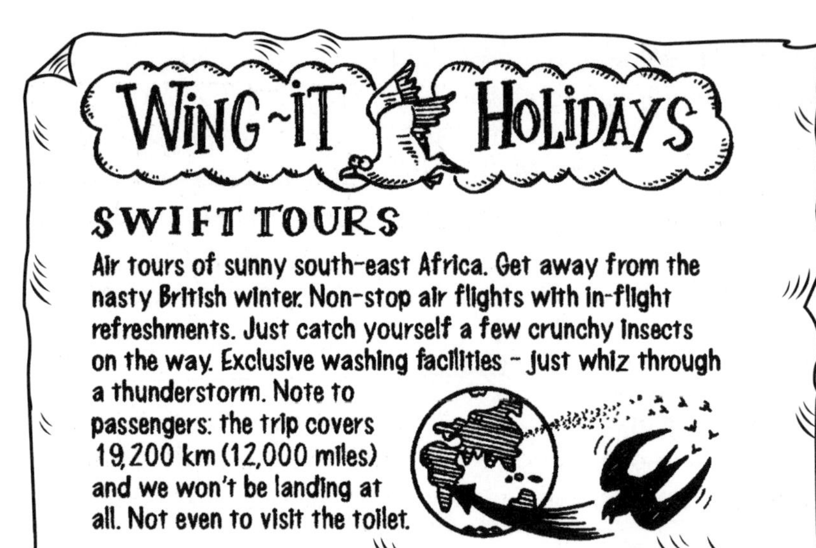

- The swift flies a long distance as it migrates, covering many kilometres. Use an atlas to help you plot its route from the UK to Kenya in southeast Africa. Record some of the countries here.

UK					Kenya

- Now find out what the average temperatures is in these countries in January. Record your data in a block graph.

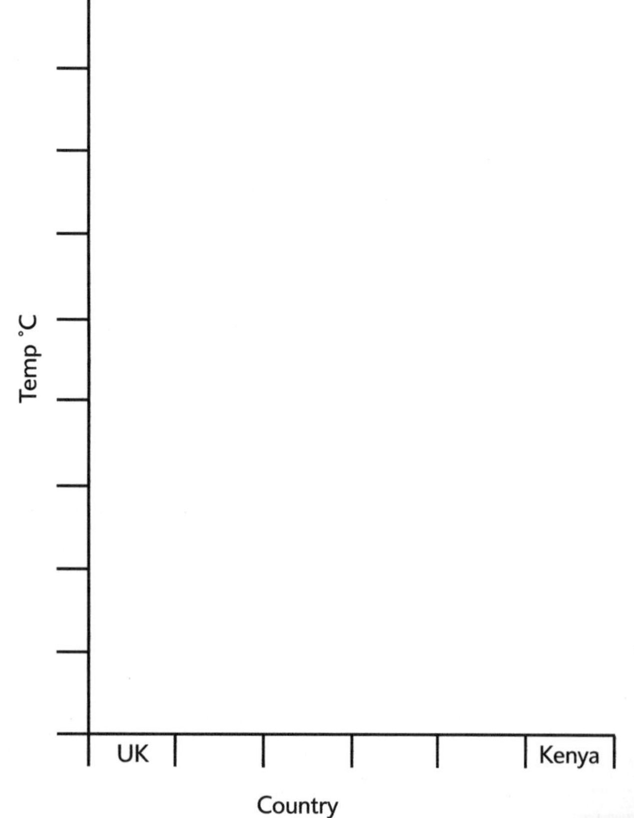

- Compare the UK's temperature at this time of year with the other countries the swift flies through. What do you notice?

____

____

____

- Why do you think the swift makes this difficult journey each year?

____

____

____

____

____

____

NAME ______________________ DATE ______________________

Conservation debate

- Changes in the Earth's climate can affect habitats.

- Climate change is not the only thing that threatens some creatures with extinction. Some animals are hunted or fished, others have not reproduced sufficiently. Some people think that these animals should be allowed to die out naturally, others work to preserve them.

- What do you think?

- Choose an animal that is threatened with extinction and write a report that weighs up both sides of the argument. Use the plan below to help you make notes.

Plan

Paragraph 1
(introduction)

Paragraph 2
(reasons for allowing the animals to die naturally or to continue hunting)

Paragraph 3
(reasons to preserve these animals)

Paragraph 4
(your own opinion)

Paragraph 5
(conclusion)

Snail's-eye view!

- Some snails see things very differently to humans as our eyes have evolved in a different way.

- Find a tube. Something about 30 cm (12 inches) long and eight cm (three inches) wide would be ideal, but the exact size doesn't matter.
- Tape some aluminium foil over one end and prick the tiniest possible hole in the middle with a sharp pin.
- Tape a piece of tracing paper over the other end.
- Then point the pinhole at a bright window or bright light. You'll see an image upside down on the tracing paper. This is how a pinhole camera works. Some snails have got eyes like this.

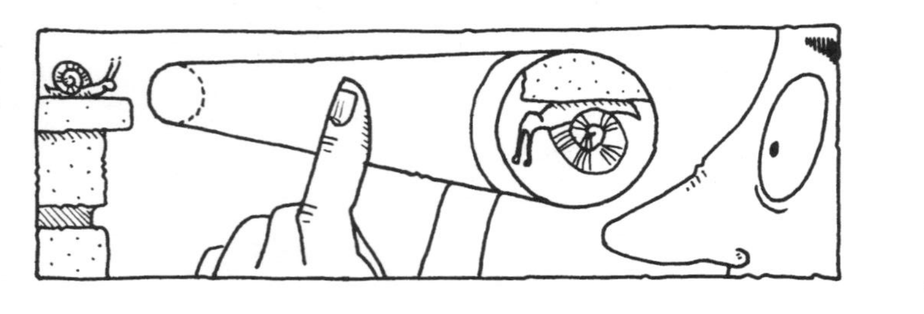

So, now you've seen the world through the eye of a snail. The picture is clear enough to tell you whether that animal lurking outside your home is a friend or an enemy – even if it's upside down.

SAFETY NOTE!
Remember, never look directly at the sun.

- Use these instructions to make a pin-hole camera.
- Use your pin-hole camera to look around you very slowly.
- Imagine that you are a snail that has taken a wrong turn and ended up in your classroom!
- Write a story for younger snails warning them of the dangers...
- The story has been started for you.

'Will everybody please SIT DOWN!'

The strange human at the front of the room shouted so loudly it made my poor shell rattle. Then, suddenly, a whole load of little humans came running through the door, dreadful noisy creatures – they were like a load of piglets! There they were, pushing and shoving their way around, I tried to move closer to the wall for safety but they were so amazingly fast compared to me...

Comparing habitats

- These creatures live in very different habitats.

Nasty home truths

1 The Australian white tree frog is a friendly little creature with a big smile on its slimy face. Clearly, this happy hopper is very pleased with its favourite home – a toilet cistern. (Before the invention of the toilet the frogs lived in smelly ponds.)

2 Snapper turtles in eastern North America are quite at home in smelly stagnant ponds or stinking sewers. It's a bad idea to go paddling in these places (as if you would!). Snapper turtles lurk in the shallows and they'd love nice pink toes for tea.

3 An octopus will live in any hollow object lying on the sea bed. They're really not fussy – for a small octopus a human skull makes a cosy little home.

4 Eagles and ospreys build large, scruffy twig nests on top of trees. Unfortunately, they also build them on electricity pylons. Sometimes a bird touches a power line and you end up with Kentucky fried eagle.

- What do creatures look for in a successful habitat? Make a list.
- Now research a typical habitat for the creatures below and compare them to your own habitat.

Rabbit Owl Horse Mouse Tuna fish

NAME ________________ DATE ________________

Keeping clean

- Some animals help others to keep clean.

CREATURE COMFORTS SERVICES DIRECTORY

HEY FISH – D'YOU FANCY A WASH AND BRUSH UP?

Let your friendly cleaner Wrasse do the job for you. We'll nibble that nasty mould and fungus away and leave your scales as good as new! Speedy personal attention assured.

"Cleaner Wrasse managed to serve a queue of 300 fish in a single session. Highly recommended."

A. Shark (Pacific Ocean)

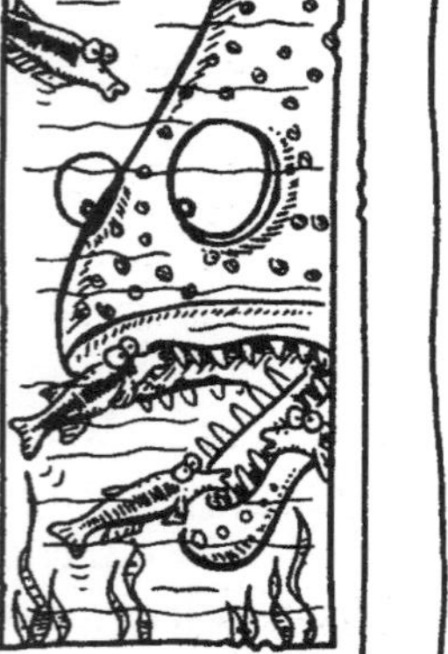

WARNING!

To all customers of Cleaner Wrasse Services: BEWARE OF CHEAP IMITATIONS! Blenny fish try to copy Cleaner Wrasse. They've even copied the stripe on our bodies. But BEWARE! As soon as they get close they'll take a bite out of you and scarper!

GOBIES' GOUPER GOB-GROOMING SERVICES

Are you a gouper fish with bad breath? Special offer – let us clean out your mouth free of charge! We'll eat those nasty bits of rotten food and we won't leave you feeling down in the mouth.

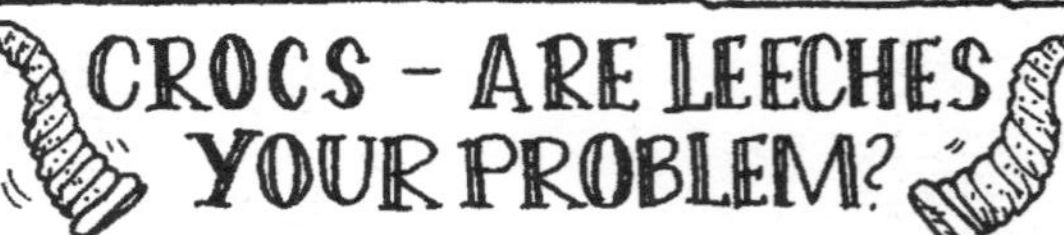

CROCS – ARE LEECHES YOUR PROBLEM?

There's nothing that spoils a good meal more than leeches clinging to your gums and sucking your blood. But spur-winged plovers have the leeches licked. Just open your mouth and we'll eat them for you. Also free danger-warning service. If you hear us chirp – there's a large, fierce animal on the way, so you'd better jump in the river!

- Other animals clean themselves. They have very different ways of doing it!
- Find out about:
  Cats
  Elephants
  Sparrows
- Make an advert for cleaning equipment that they may find useful!

Creature cleaners

FISH FACTS

The archer fish of India, Australia and south–east Asia has an unusual secret weapon. A built-in water pistol. This 2 cm long fish spits water with deadly accuracy at passing insects.

- Fish come in all shapes and sizes. Take a look at the fish fact to the left.

- Read the fish facts below and decide which are true and which are false.

Far-fetched fish facts

1 A trumpet fish hitches a ride on a larger but harmless parrot fish. When the trumpet fish spots a small fish to eat it hops off to make a quick killing! TRUE/FALSE

2 Vicious blue fish attack schools of other fish off the Eastern coasts of North America. The brutal blues kill more than ten times the fish they can eat. They guzzle up to 40 at a time and then sick them up so they can go on eating! TRUE/FALSE

3 The halitosis haddock has a deadly and unusual weapon – its disgusting, smelly breath. When a smaller fish comes by, the horrible haddock breathes a cloud of poisonous bubbles to overwhelm its prey. TRUE/FALSE

4 The angler fish has its own fishing rod complete with a small worm-like object that dangles just above its mouth. When another fish comes to investigate the bait the angler fish snaps up its catch. TRUE/FALSE.

5 The scissors fish has jaws just like a pair of scissors and it uses these fearsome weapons to slice up its prey. It's even been known to snip through the lines of deep-sea anglers. TRUE/FALSE.

6 The deep-sea viper fish has 1,350 lights inside its mouth. They twinkle in the ocean depths and little fish flock to see the lovely spectacle. Once the fish are inside its mouth the viper fish closes its giant gob. End of show. TRUE/FALSE.

- Try researching your own fish facts and adding some false 'facts' to fool your friends.

NAME ______________________ DATE ______________________

Life cycles

- As tadpoles grow, their bodies change.
- Look at picture number 1. This shows the tadpole when it has hatched from the egg.
- What did the egg look like?
- Where did the egg come from?
- Draw a cartoon prequel to illustrate this information, cut out all the pictures and arrange them in order to show the life cycle of the frog or toad.

Dr Frog and Mr Tadpole

1 The tadpole hatches from eggs and gobbles up its unlucky brothers and sisters.

2 But in a few weeks it develops into a very different looking but equally repulsive adult.

3 The adult frog doesnt eat its own kind but it does grab flies with its long, sticky tongue.

4 Most amphibia spend the winter buried in mud at the bottom of lakes and ponds.

Dr Frog and Mr Tadpole – the prequel!

1	2
3	4

Inside an egg

- Some creatures start life inside an egg.

Sometime after mating, female animals give birth. Mammals produce live young but some other groups of animals lay eggs. Dare you discover the secrets hidden inside an egg?

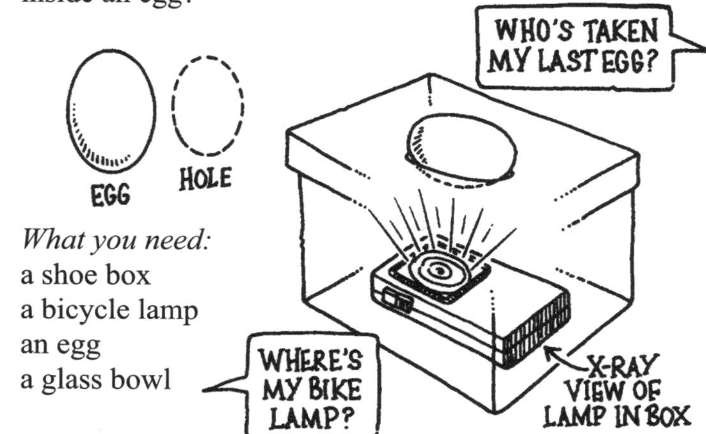

What you need:
a shoe box
a bicycle lamp
an egg
a glass bowl

All you do is:
1 Draw round the egg on the box lid. Cut a hole just large enough for the egg to lie in without falling through.
2 Put the lamp in the box, switch it on and replace the lid. Place the egg in its hole.
3 Darken the room.
4 You should be able to see the yolk inside the egg.

5 Lightly tap the egg on the side of the bowl and allow its contents to slide into the bowl. Note: That's into the *bowl* not on the floor.

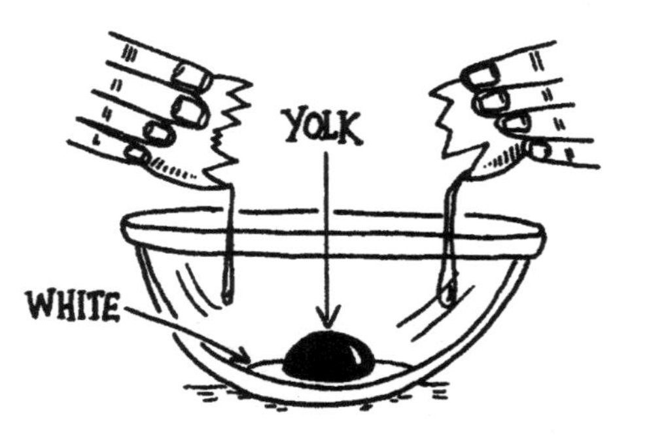

6 The egg's contents consists of the yellow bit or 'yolk' and the clear slimy bit or 'white', or to use its scientific name – albumen (al-bu-men). Although you won't be able to see this, the yolk is held in position by two cords.

From your observations can you guess how the chick manages to breathe inside the egg?
a) It breathes air that passes through the shell.
b) It doesn't need to breathe before it hatches.
c) There must be an air bubble inside the egg.

- How many animals do you know that start life inside an egg? Make a list and illustrate what happens next in their life cycle.

NAME ____________________ DATE ____________________

Reproduction

- When the baby chicks grow they will grow into female or male chickens.
- When they are adults they will reproduce.
- Eventually the adults grow old and die.
- Not all creatures start their lives outside their mother in an egg!

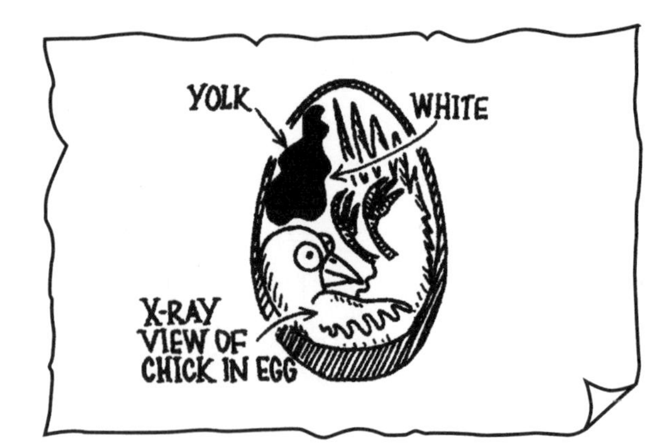

- Fill in the picture boxes and finish the sentences.

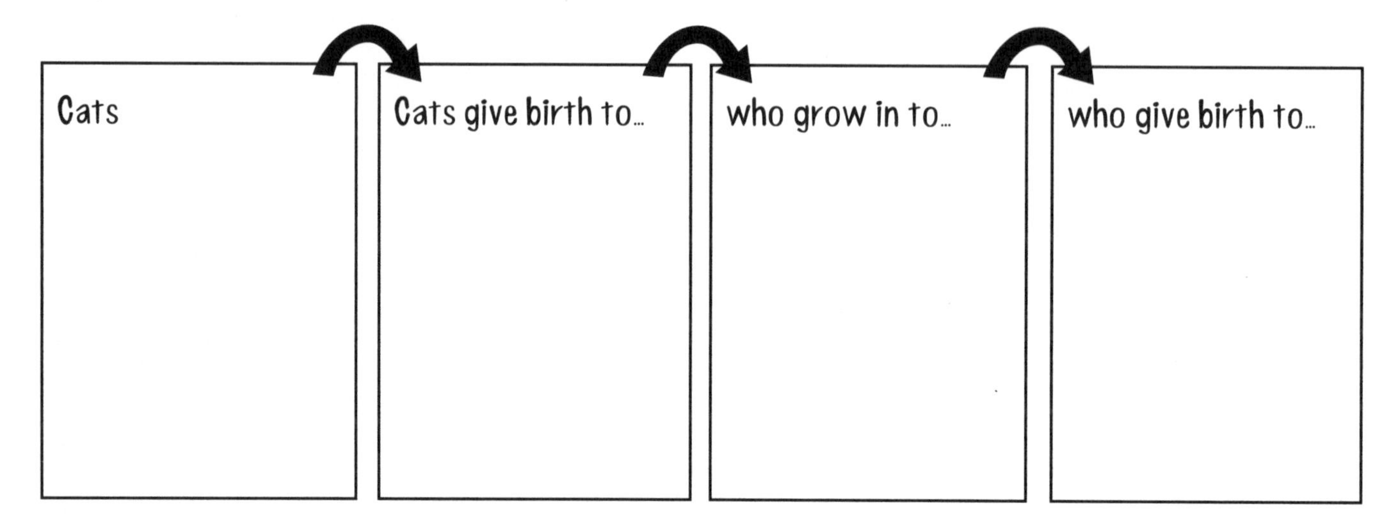

- How about you? Try the same with humans!

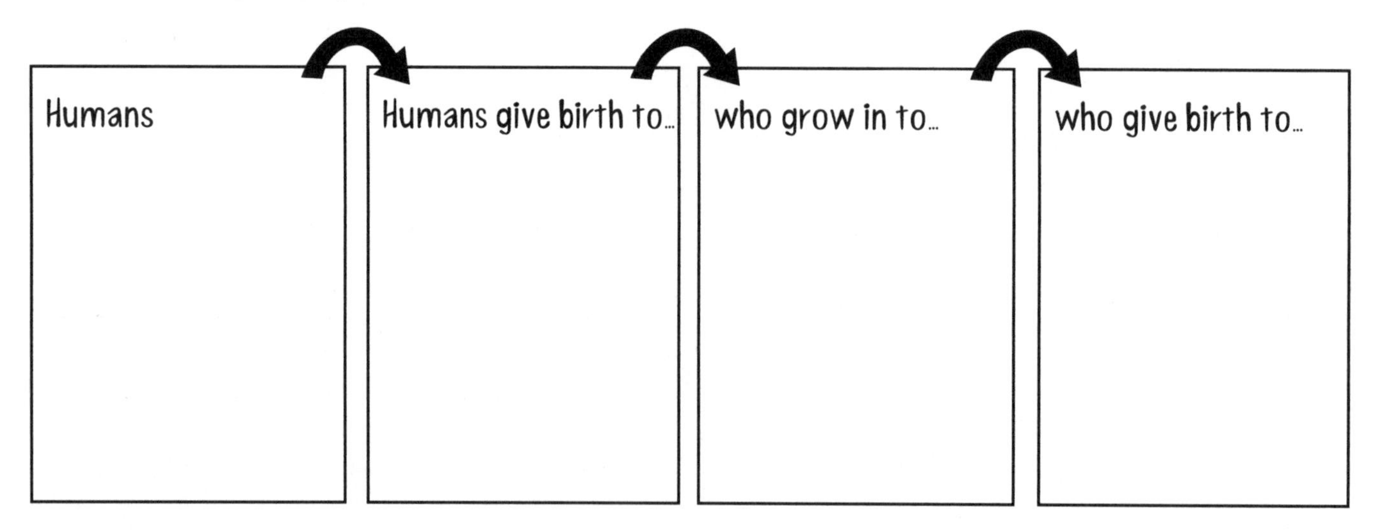

- Kangaroos belong to the marsupial family. Find out how their lives begin and draw a life cycle for them.

NAME ______________________ DATE ______________________

RABBIT CALCULATIONS

- Rabbits can produce around 50 babies a year.
- Brown rabbits live up to six years old. White and black rabbits each live for around two years.
- Calculate:

1. How many babies a brown rabbit might produce in her lifetime.
2. How many babies a white or black rabbit might produce in her lifetime.
3. What is the difference between these two numbers?

- Research reproduction rates for these mammals:

Elephant Hamster Cat Dolphin

1. How many babies does a female elephant produce in a white rabbit's lifetime? __________
2. How many kittens make up the average litter? __________
3. How long is the female dolphin pregnant for? __________
4. How many hamsters will a female hamster have produced in this time? __________
5. How long does each of these mammals live on average? __________

- Add all your numbers together for a grand total. __________

NAME ______________________ DATE ______________________

Food chains

- All creatures are part of a food chain.
- Take a look at this food chain and add your own captions to explain what is going on.
- What did you have for lunch today? Draw and label it on this plate.
- Write and draw a food chain for two things from your plate.

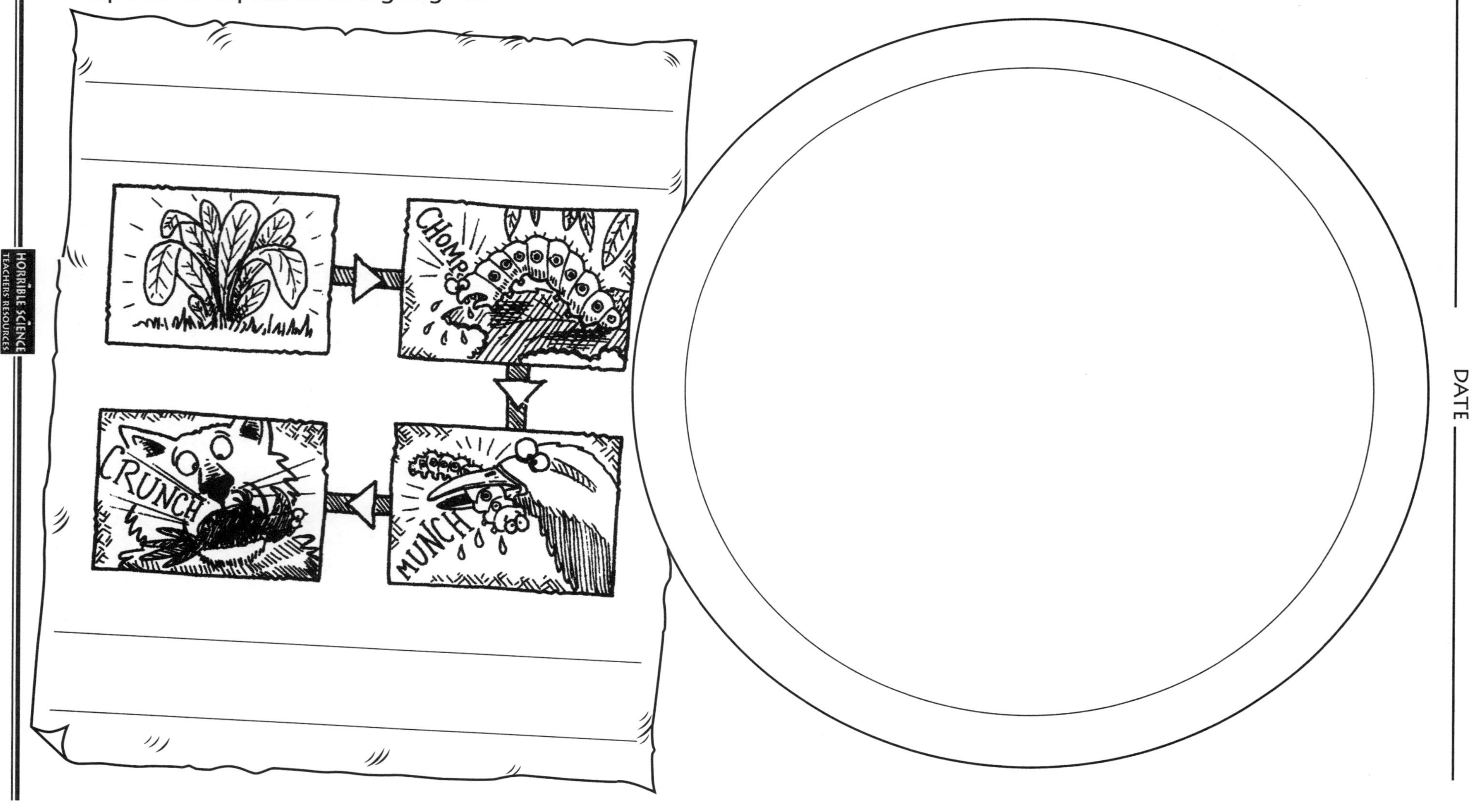

Hunting

Lion hunting tips
The lionesses in a pride (group of lions) hunt together. (The lazy males don't take part.)

1 Your pride of lionesses stalk a herd of gazelles (small antelope). From what direction do you approach?
a) With the wind at your back so that the gazelles can smell you. This will scare them so much they won't be able to defend themselves.
b) With the wind blowing in your face so the gazelles can't smell you.
c) From the direction of the sun so that the gazelles are dazzled.

2 Your pride splits into two groups. What do you do next?
a) One group charges the gazelles and chases them towards the second group waiting in ambush.
b) One group goes after the gazelles and the others chase some nearby zebra. This doubles the chance of catching something.
c) One group chases gazelles and the others keep watch for marauding hyenas that might try to steal the meat.

3 You select a gazelle to attack. Which one do you choose?
a) The biggest – more meat for you.
b) The smallest – less likely to put up a fight.
c) The weakest – easier to catch.

4 The males invite themselves to the feast. While you and your sisters have been hunting the males have been lazing about in the sun. Now they're hungry. So who gets the lion's share?
a) The lionesses, followed by the cubs. The males are given a few scraps. Serves 'em right for not helping.
b) The males take the best bits. The lionesses and the cubs get what's left. If they're lucky.
c) The cubs. After all they need the food to help them grow.

5 A new male chases away the old males in your pride. He cruelly kills and eats your cubs. What do you do?
a) Run for the hills.
b) Kill him and eat his body.
c) Make friends with him.

6 In the dry season there's little food. What do you eat?
a) Other lions
b) Fish, insects, lizards, mice and the odd tortoise.
c) Bones buried for just such an emergency.

NAME ______________________ DATE ______________________

Food web

- All creatures are part of a food web and all these food webs start with a plant.

A food web (nothing to do with spiders) links the food chains in a particular habitat. So you might end up with something like this:

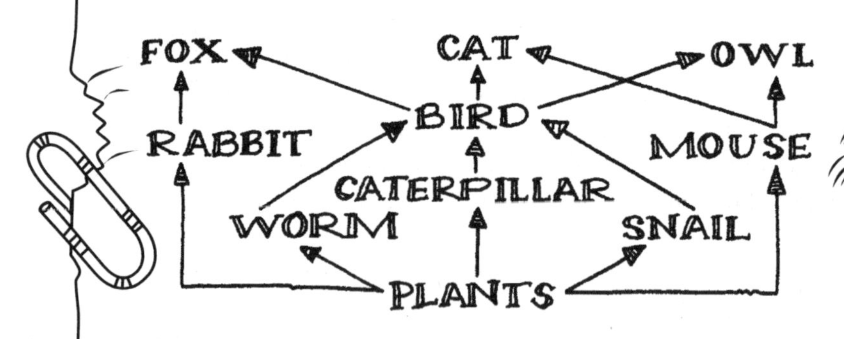

Animals depend on each other and on plants. Take away the plants, and the bugs and rabbits and mice starve. If they disappear the animals that eat them will go hungry too.

Strangely enough if the top animals in the web disappear there can be nasty results too. If the fox died out more rabbits would survive to breed and multiply. Good news for rabbits? Not necessarily. The rampaging rabbits guzzle plants. This is bad news for the bugs, birds, mice and other animals that depend on plants for food and shelter. And of course, the rabbits end up starving too.

- Sea creatures are also part of the food web for their watery habitat.
- Research and draw a food web for sea creatures. Include any creatures above water that eat them, such as seagulls and humans!

Sea creatures food web

NAME ______________________ DATE ______________________

WHO EATS WHAT?

Disgusting diets
Each animal has a favourite type of food. Animals that only eat plants are called herbivores (not vegetarians – that's a name for human herbivores). Animals that only eat meat are called carnivores. And creatures that eat both (including humans who enjoy meat and two veg) are called omnivores. Simple, isn't it? But some animals also scoff sickening side dishes. Could you match the animal to the horrible things it eats?

- Draw eight different creatures in these cards and cut them out. Include a mixture of herbivores, carnivores and omnivores.
- Draw their foods on another piece of paper.
- Challenge your partner to match the animal to the food.

Extinct or endangered?

- Dinosaurs were amongst the earliest creatures to live on Earth. They dominated the planet for 150 million years before becoming extinct over 65 million years ago.
- There is no definite answer to why dinosaurs died out.
- However, we do know why the creatures opposite became extinct.
- Which of these creatures are extinct and which are endangered?

• The dodo. Once lived on the tiny island of Mauritius in the Indian Ocean. It was especially happy because it had no enemies on the island. Until, of course, man arrived and brought rats, cats and dogs. The poor old dodo had no wings, so it couldn't fly off. The last dodo was so slow, it bit the dust as long ago as 1680.

• Steller's sea cow. A tame and gentle creature. Named after George Steller, a German naturalist who discovered the sea cow when he was shipwrecked in 1742. The last sea cow was spotted in 1769, and it followed the fate of the rest of its family… to be eaten by sailors.

Dodo R.I.P. 1680 SURVIVAL WAS A NO NO FOR THE DODO

Steller's sea cow R.I.P. 1769 TENDER, TAME... TASTY

• The Tasmanian wolf looked like a smaller, slimmer version of the European wolf, but was striped and used to carry its babies in a pouch, like a kangaroo. Sheep farmers on the island of Tasmania were furious when it took a fancy to their flocks, so they wiped it out. The last survivor died in Hobart Zoo in 1936.

• The dusky seaside sparrow. Once upon a time, the Cape Kennedy space centre was just a vast stretch of marshland. It was a sparrow's paradise. But then the rockets went up, and the bird's came down as the development of the site wiped out their food supply. Scientists couldn't save them, and this sparrow made its final flight in 1984.

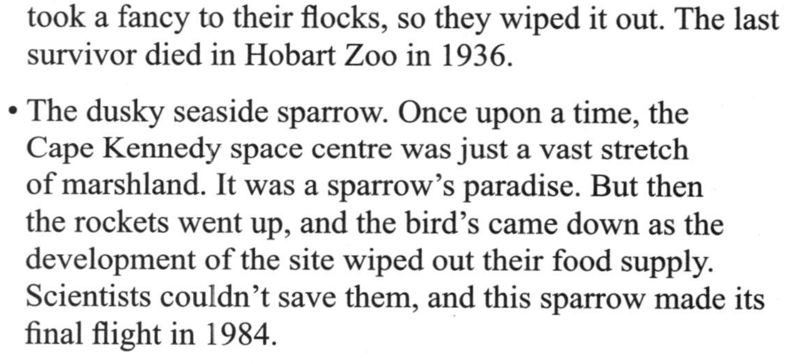

Giant panda Rabbit Tiger Passenger pigeon

- Find out as much as you can and write a guide explaining how we can help creatures that are threatened with extinction.

The tiger must die! 1

- Some animals are dangerous to humans.
- In Victorian times tigers were hunted and shot because people were scared of them. They used their skin for rugs.
- By 1972 only about 1,800 Tigers were left! Conservationists persuaded people to stop hunting them. People still argue about whether this is a good idea or not...

India/Nepal border 1978

'The tiger must die. I could have shot it myself!' cried the Forest Park Director thumping his desk.

'You don't understand,' said Arjan Singh the tiger expert. He was slightly built and balding and right now his brow was creased with worry.

The Director's mouth set in a hard line. He wiped the sweat off his fleshy face with a damp handkerchief. It was very hot, even though the blinds were drawn and the ceiling fan whirred lazily. 'No, Mr Singh, it's you who doesn't understand. Let's review the facts, shall we? On 3 April a man disappeared in the forest. Tiger victim number one. What was left of him after the tiger had finished didn't even fill a shoe box. Three days later another man went missing. I saw the tiger eating his body. I shouted but the monster took no notice. I wish I'd shot the tiger then and there.'

His finger curled round an imaginary gun trigger.

'But tigers are protected,' said Arjan Singh, 'you can't go around shooting them.'

'Human beings must be protected too!' roared the Director. 'Two men are dead and you're trying to teach me my job!'

'But you don't understand!' repeated Arjan Singh desperately. 'Tigers only attack humans because they have to.'

'What do you mean they *have to*?!' spluttered the Director wildly, his eyes blazing with fury.

'Tigers don't normally attack humans,' said the naturalist. 'But humans have wiped out all the tiger's natural prey such as deer and wild pigs. The tiger was starving and there were humans in the forest. The tiger was feeding to stay alive.'

'On human flesh,' said the Director harshly.

The tiger must die! 2

Arjan Singh took a deep breath and tried again. 'Remember, tigers are protected by law. Instead of killing the tiger can't we try another way? Why can't we leave out a few buffalo for it to eat? Then the tiger won't be hungry. And if it's not hungry it won't attack people.'

The Director sighed bitterly. 'Mr Singh, I'll be frank. If I had my way that tiger of yours would have been dead meat days ago. But my bosses seem to agree with you about not shooting the animal. So I suppose I've got to think your idea over.'

But he didn't sound convinced.

A few days passed without a decision from the Director. And meanwhile the tiger struck again. Arjan Singh felt his heart sink as he examined the paw marks.

'Yes, I'm afraid it's the same tiger,' he told the wildlife warden who had come with him.

'Well, Mr Singh,' said the man grimly. 'Looks like the Director will get his way after all. That tiger's a goner now.'

A few metres along the path made by the tiger as it dragged its prey, lay a gory human head. It was all that remained of the tiger's latest victim.

Arjan Singh imagined the Park Director's scornful voice. He would say: 'I told you so! It's your fault – if I'd had my way that man would still be alive.'

The naturalist dreaded the next meeting. Could anything save the tiger now?

What do you think happened next?

a) The Park Director got his way. The tiger was hunted down and shot.

b) Arjan Singh got his way. The Director agreed to put food out for the tiger and it never again attacked people.

c) The tiger was shot with a tranquillizing dart and moved to an area far away from humans.

- Choose which ending to the story you think is most likely, explaining your reasons.
- Finish the story using your chosen ending. Write in the same style as 'The tiger must die!' using speech and paragraphs.

The tiger must die! 3

- 'The tiger must die!' is a true story.

Terrible tigers
From its nose to the tip of its stripy tail the average tiger is 2.9 metres (9 feet 6 inches) and weighs 204 kg (32 stone) – that's the weight of three grown men. In the 19th century, Victorian writers gave the tiger a bad press. They saw the tiger as a treacherous enemy that took its victims by surprise. The Hon James Inglis wrote:

19th-century hunters enjoyed 'bagging' tigers and they even got paid for their horrible pastime by the Indian government! Many tigers ended up as grisly tiger-skin rugs. But the hunters were far too deadly for the tigers. By 1972 there were only about 1,800 tigers left alive in the whole of India. Hunting was banned in 1971 and thanks to a massive conservation effort, tiger numbers began to increase in some areas. But the naturalists' work raised a nasty dilemma. What should be done when a tiger attacks humans? Was it ever right to kill a tiger?

- People still argue about whether it is right to kill dangerous animals. What do you think?
- Write a play based on the story. Split it into scenes and set it out as a play script, giving your characters interesting dialogue and stage directions.
- The play has been started for you...

Scene 1: The forest park director's office

Park Director: That tiger must die! I could have shot him myself! (*Thumps desk loudly*)

Arjan Singh: But you don't understand, there are hardly any tigers left as it is! We only managed to stop people hunting them and using them as carpet a few years ago! Those Victorians shot most of them in the last century – what will happen if we start again now? (*He paces about, looking very worried*)

Park Director: (*Mopping his face with a hanky*) Honestly, Mr Singh! How many times have I got to explain this to you? The creature is a menace! A danger to humans, I mean, look at the facts...

- Carry on the script and perform it for your class or school.

WORD SEARCH CLUES

- The words you will be looking for appear in these clues.
- They are written in CAPITAL LETTERS.

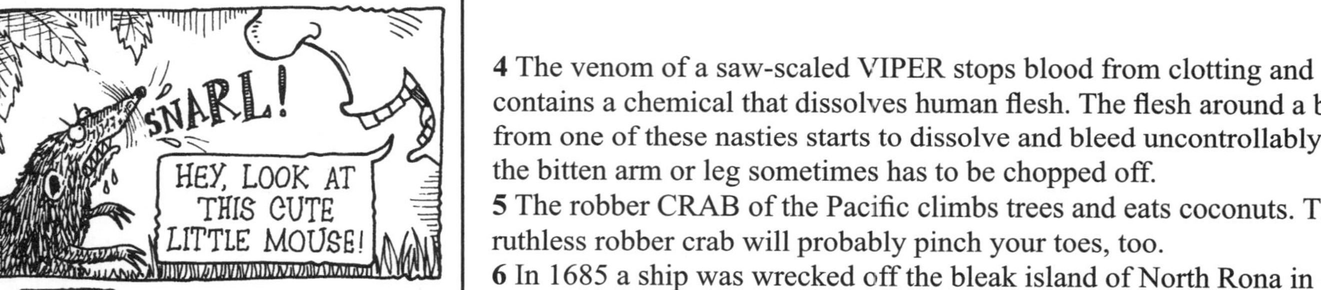

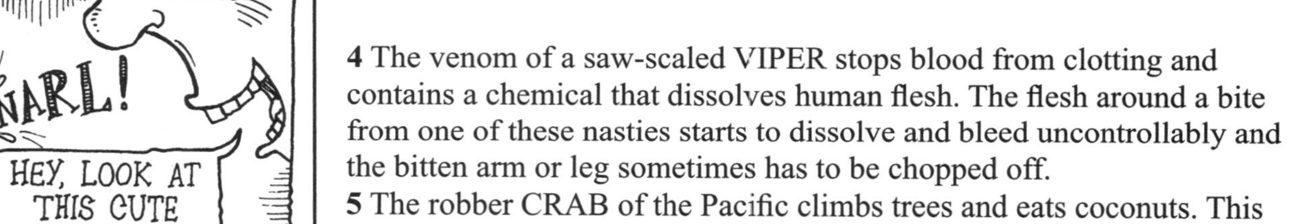

1 The most vicious hunter in the world is said by many biologists to be the short-tailed SHREW (a mouse-like animal) from North America. It has a poisonous bite deadly enough to kill 200 mice.

2 If a CROCODILE attacks you the best thing to do is grip its snout and hold its jaws shut. The muscles that open the croc's mouth are quite weak and even a puny human can hold the mouth shut.

3 The Portuguese man o' war is a type of JELLYFISH. Its sting can stop the nerves working and in the Bahamas and Majorca local people believe that the best treatment is to get someone to pee on your injuries.

4 The venom of a saw-scaled VIPER stops blood from clotting and contains a chemical that dissolves human flesh. The flesh around a bite from one of these nasties starts to dissolve and bleed uncontrollably and the bitten arm or leg sometimes has to be chopped off.

5 The robber CRAB of the Pacific climbs trees and eats coconuts. This ruthless robber crab will probably pinch your toes, too.

6 In 1685 a ship was wrecked off the bleak island of North Rona in Scotland. The ship's RATs swam ashore and ate all the islanders' food. Heavy seas prevented the islanders escaping and they all starved to death.

7 The sharp-beaked FINCH of the Galapagos islands eats seeds but it's also a vampire, pecking holes in the wings of nesting sea birds and sucking their blood.

8 The OKAPI (a zebra-like creature that's actually more closely related to the giraffe) can wash its face and ears with its 36 cm (14 inch)

NAME ____________________ DATE ____________________

WORDSEARCH GRID

Wordsearch

(One point per word, total score eight points.)

H	S	I	F	Y	L	L	E	J
B	A	R	C	S	F	E	I	V
C	W	E	R	H	S	A	T	H
L	I	P	A	K	O	K	A	P
E	L	I	D	O	C	O	R	C
J	E	V	H	C	N	I	F	O

Bonus question

Comohoridae (co-mo-hor-rid-day) fish live in Lake Baykal in Siberia, Russia. Over a quarter of their body is oily fat and if you leave one in the sun it will melt. What other unusual quality do they have?

a) They can walk on water.

b) They can swim backwards.

c) They have see-through bodies.

- Now use all your Horrible Science knowledge about animals to make your own word search and write some interesting clues. Don't forget to set a bonus question!
- Try it on your partner.

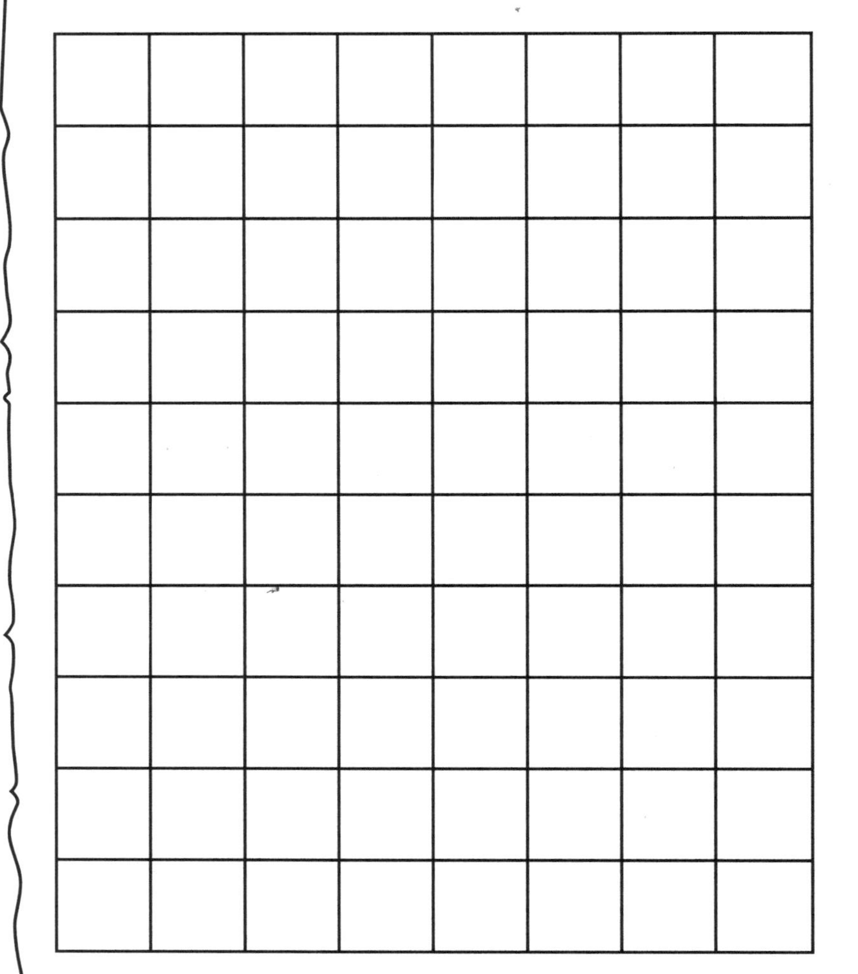

BEARS BEWARE QUIZ!

Bears BEWARE! quiz
North American bears are ferocious. The black bear grows three times heavier than a man ... and then there's the really BIG bears. A grizzly bear once bit an Alaskan hunter's *head* in half *and that's after the bear had been shot through the heart*. It must have been a grizzly sight.

Here's a list of bear safety instructions. All you have to do is sort them into DOs and DON'Ts.

Bear safety instructions

- Check your answers.
- Now choose one of these animals and write safety instructions for it.

Lion Eagle Fox Elephant Shark

- Challenge your partner to sort out your instructions into DOs and DON'Ts.

NAME ______________________ DATE ______________________

Animal spotter's quiz

Can you match the animals to their correct names? (Clue: All these animals have seriously misleading names.)

Animal names
a) Glass-snake
b) Crayfish
c) Ring-tailed cat
d) Naked mole rat
e) Firefly
f) Civet cat
g) Horned toad

Draw your animals here:

- Now research some more unusual animals of your own.
- Can your partner match the names to the animals?

Write their names here:

FISHY ACCUMULATOR QUIZ

This true story is an accumulator quiz. Ask someone to read you one question at a time. If you choose the right answer you can continue with the quiz but if you get any question wrong you have to STOP the quiz! You get one point for each correct answer.

In December 1999 a girl saw a goldfish on the hearth rug. She ran and told her mum. Her mum was astonished and quickly put the goldfish in a bowl of water.

MUM, MUM, QUICK!

HURRY UP!

1 What was the fish doing on the rug? (Clue: The family didn't have a goldfish.)

a) It had come down the chimney and bounced off the fire.
b) The neighbour's cat had brought it in.
c) It had leapt in through the window.

Answer (one point):
a) If you got that right you can go on.

2 OK, so how did the fish get into the chimney?

a) Someone was playing a practical joke.
b) A bird had caught the fish and dropped it.
c) The fish had been sucked up from its pond by a freak whirlwind.

Answer (one point):
b) The bird is thought to have been a heron. If you got that right you can go on.

3 So what happened to the fish?

a) The fish died and its remains were fed to the neighbour's cat.
b) The fish was fine and it found a good home.
c) The fish was very ill and it turned white with fear.

Answer (one point):
b) The fish just had a few marks from the bird's beak. If you got that right here's one more question, this time about goldfish and scientists…

4 A scientist tried to find out if a goldfish could become seasick by making waves in its bowl. (By the way, this was another goldfish.) What did he find?

a) Seasick? Huh – you must be joking, we're talking FISH here. They *love* waves!
b) Yes, they do get seasick – and I expect the goldfish turned into a *green*fish.
c) The goldfish leapt out of its bowl and slapped the scientist on the nose.

Answer (one point):
b) Goldfish live in rivers – they're not used to waves.

- How did you do?
- Try it on your partner.
- Now use all your Horrible Science knowledge about fish to make your own fishy accumulator quiz.